TOPICS IN MATHEMATICS

Areas and Logarithms

A. I. Markushevich

Translated and adapted from the first Russian edition (1952) by

RONALD S. TOCZEK *and* REUBEN SANDLER

SURVEY OF

RECENT EAST EUROPEAN MATHEMATICAL LITERATURE

A project conducted by

ALFRED L. PUTNAM *and* IZAAK WIRSZUP

*Department of Mathematics,
The University of Chicago, under a
grant from the National Science Foundation*

D. C. HEATH AND COMPANY   BOSTON

Library of Congress Catalog Card Number: 61-17844

Printed June 1966

PREFACE TO THE AMERICAN EDITION

THE AIM of this booklet is to develop the theory of logarithms from a geometric point of view. This is done by considering a special kind of "curvilinear trapezoid" and defining logarithms as areas of such curvilinear trapezoids. The basic properties of logarithms are then deduced from the properties of the areas of these figures. The development is facilitated by the introduction of certain simple concepts and results from integral calculus.

The reader need not have had any previous experience with logarithms or calculus. Only an acquaintance with polynomial functions and their graphic representation, geometric progressions, and the concept of a limit is required.

CONTENTS

CONTENTS

Areas and Logarithms

1. Areas

1. CURVILINEAR TRAPEZOIDS

In this booklet we shall study functions. A function may be described as a rule by which one can determine some number y when given a number x. Many functions are given by formulas. For example, the formula $y = x^2$ defines a function of x; for each number x, the corresponding value of y is obtained by squaring x. If $x = 3$, then $y = 9$.

The formula $y = \dfrac{1}{x}$ defines another function. Here, for x different from zero, the corresponding value of y is the reciprocal of x; if $x = 2$, then $y = \frac{1}{2}$; if $x = -\frac{1}{3}$, then $y = -3$. This function is not defined for $x = 0$. Some functions are defined for all numbers x, but others are not. When the student is given a function, he should ask himself for which numbers it is defined.

In algebra, the student has learned how to denote numbers by letters in order to work with numbers without specifying exactly what the numbers are. Now we shall sometimes want to speak of functions without indicating the particular functions being considered. We usually denote functions by the letters f, g, h, but we may use other letters.

If f is a function and x is a number (for which the function is defined), then we shall let the symbol $f(x)$ denote the number y which the function gives us. Hence, we frequently write

$$y = f(x),$$

which is read "y equals f of x."

Because it is easier to think in pictures than in more abstract terms such as functions, we shall frequently represent functions graphically. To do this, we construct a *coordinate system:* Choose a point O in the plane and call it the *origin*. From O draw two mutually perpendicular lines Ox and Oy—the *coordinate axes* (Fig. 1). Ox is called the *x-axis* and Oy the *y-axis*. Now select a unit of length. It is easy to establish a one-to-one correspondence between pairs of numbers

(x, y) and points in the plane (that is, for each pair of numbers there is exactly one point, and conversely): Given a pair of numbers (x, y), first measure off the value of x on the x-axis to the right of O if x is positive, or to the left of O if x is negative. From the point so obtained, erect a perpendicular to the x-axis, which will be parallel to the y-axis. Measure off the value of y on this perpendicular, going up from the x-axis if y is positive or down if it is negative. The point we reach corresponds to the pair of numbers (x, y); x is called the *abscissa* of the point and y is the *ordinate*. The pair (x, y) are the *coordinates* of the point. Note that the coordinates of O are $(0, 0)$.

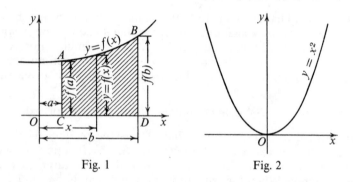

Fig. 1   Fig. 2

Now, if we have a function $y = f(x)$, we can represent it graphically by considering those points in the plane whose coordinates (x, y) are related by the equation $y = f(x)$, that is, the points $(x, f(x))$. The set of all such points is called the *graph of the function* $y = f(x)$. For example, the graph of the function $y = x^2$ is the parabola shown in Fig. 2.

In this booklet we shall study *continuous* functions only. A good approximate notion of continuity is contained in the statement that a function is continuous if its graph can be drawn without lifting the pencil from the paper.[1]

Let us take two arbitrary points A and B on the graph (Fig. 1) and drop perpendiculars AC and BD from them to the x-axis. We obtain the figure $ACDB$; such a figure may be called a *curvilinear trapezoid*. If the curve AB happens to be a line segment not parallel to the x-axis, we obtain an ordinary trapezoid. If, however, AB is a straight line segment parallel to Ox, we obtain a rectangle. Thus, a trapezoid and a rectangle may be thought of as special cases of a curvilinear trapezoid.

---

[1] A precise definition of a continuous function may be found in any good calculus text.

The graph of the function represented in Fig. 1 lies above the x-axis. This occurs only when the values of the function are positive numbers. If the values of the function were negative, the curve would lie below the x-axis (Fig. 3). In this booklet we shall consider the area of a curvilinear trapezoid to be positive if the figure lies above the x-axis and negative if it lies below it.

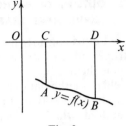

Fig. 3

It is possible for a function to have different signs for different values of x. Then its graph lies partially above the x-axis, and partially below; such a situation is depicted in Fig. 4. Here the area of the curvilinear trapezoid $A'C'D'B'$ must be taken to be negative,

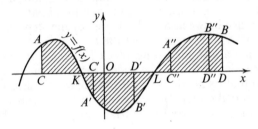

Fig. 4

and the area of $A''C''D''B''$, positive. If we take the points A and B as shown in the figure and from them drop the perpendiculars AC and BD to the x-axis, then between these perpendiculars we have the figure which is shaded in Fig. 4. This figure is called, as before, a curvilinear trapezoid; it is bounded by the arc $AKA'B'LA''B''B$, the two line segments AC and BD, and the segment CD on the x-axis. Let us take its area to be the sum of the areas of the figures ACK, $KA'B'L$, and $LA''BD$, the areas of the first and third being positive and the area of the second, negative.

The reader can easily see that according to these assumptions the area of the whole curvilinear trapezoid $ACDB$ can be negative, or positive, or—in certain cases—equal to zero. For example, the graph of the function $y = ax$ $(a > 0)$ is a straight line; the area of the figure $ACDB$ (Fig. 5) is, therefore, positive when $OD > OC$, negative when $OD < OC$, and, finally, equal to zero when $OD = OC$.

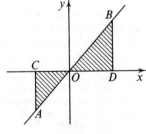

Fig. 5

3

2. OUTLINE OF METHOD FOR FINDING THE AREAS OF CURVILINEAR TRAPEZOIDS

Let us consider the problem of finding the area S of a curvilinear trapezoid. In various mathematical, physical, and mechanical problems the need to compute such areas arises so frequently that a whole field of mathematics has arisen, the integral calculus, which studies the methods of solving this problem. Let us outline a two-part general method, which we shall use here. In the first part we shall find approximate values of the area, making the error of the approximation arbitrarily small; in the second part we shall pass from the approximate values of the area to the exact value.

We begin by considering, instead of the curvilinear trapezoid $ACDB$, a step-like figure as seen in Fig. 6. We can easily compute the area of the step-like figure: it is equal to the sum of the areas of the rectangles. We shall use this sum to approximate the area S.

The difference between S and the area of the step-like figure is a certain "error" α; this error is just the total area of the curvilinear triangles which are shaded solid black in our illustration. To estimate this error, let us choose the widest rectangle and extend its vertical sides so that its height is equal to the largest value of the function in the interval under consideration (in Fig. 6, this is $\overline{BD}$). Then let us move all of the curvilinear triangles parallel to the x-axis so

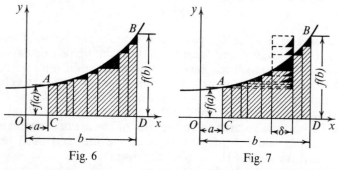

Fig. 6   Fig. 7

that they will lie within this rectangle; they will form inside it a "toothed" figure resembling the edge of a saw (Fig. 7). Since this figure is completely contained within the rectangle, the error α, which is the sum of the areas of the teeth of the saw,[1] must be less than the

---

[1] The curve in Fig. 6 and 7 is ascending; that is, it runs uphill as x moves to the right. If the curve were more complicated with successive ascents and descents (see, for example, Fig. 4), then the curvilinear triangles, upon being moved into one rectangle, might overlap one another, so that the sum of their areas might be greater than the area of the rectangle. To handle this more complicated case, we divide the whole figure into sections so that in each section the curve either ascends or descends (but not both), and then carry out our process for each individual section.

4

area of the rectangle. If the length of the base of this rectangle is denoted by δ (the Greek letter "delta"), then we have $|\alpha| < \delta \cdot \overline{BD}$. Hence it follows that we can make the error α arbitrarily small if we take the rectangles in Fig. 6 so narrow that the base δ of the widest of them is sufficiently small. For example, if $\overline{BD} = 20$, and if we want the area of the step-like figure to differ from S by less than 0.001, then it suffices to take $\delta \cdot \overline{BD} = 20\delta$ smaller than 0.001, that is, $\delta < 0.00005$; then

$$|\alpha| < \delta \cdot \overline{BD} < 0.001.$$

However, no matter how small we make δ, we always obtain a certain error α—even though it be very small; for the area of the curvilinear trapezoid is not actually equal to the area of the step-like figure.

The second part of our solution involves passage to the limit. We assume that we are considering not one or two, but an infinite number of step-like figures. We take greater and greater numbers of rectangles, increasing their number without limit, and, at the same time, making the width δ of the widest rectangle smaller and smaller; that is, δ approaches closer and closer to zero. Then the error α will become progressively smaller, approaching ever nearer to zero. Thus, we obtain the required area S by calculating the limit of the areas of the step-like figures. (The areas of the step-like figures approach the desired area S.)

3. AREAS OF THE SIMPLEST CURVILINEAR TRAPEZOIDS

Let us continue as in the previous section and compute the area of a curvilinear trapezoid where the function $y = f(x)$ is a power of x with a nonnegative integral exponent: $y = x^k$. For the exponents $k = 0, 1, 2$ we obtain the functions: $y = x^0 = 1$, $y = x^1$, $y = x^2$. One can easily draw their graphs: they are the straight line

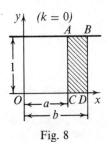

Fig. 8

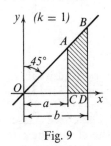

Fig. 9

parallel to the x-axis lying 1 unit above it (Fig. 8), the bisector of the angle xOy (Fig. 9), and the parabola (Fig. 10).

5

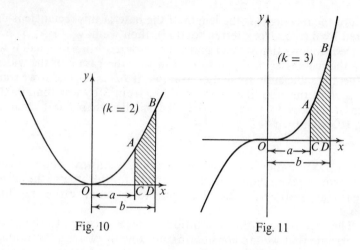

Fig. 10   Fig. 11

If we take higher powers of x, we obtain the functions $y = x^3$, $y = x^4$, and $y = x^5$, whose graphs are shown in Fig. 11, 12, and 13.

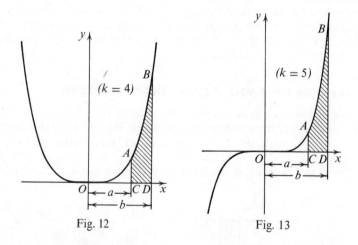

Fig. 12   Fig. 13

If k is an odd number, the curve is symmetric with respect to the point O (Fig. 9, 11, 13); if k is even, the curve is symmetric with respect to the y-axis (Fig. 8, 10, 12).

If $k \geq 1$, the curve passes through the point O. Moreover, the larger k is, the closer the curve lies to the x-axis in the neighborhood of the point O, and at the same time, the more rapidly it rises or falls as it moves far away from the point O.

In each of Fig. 8–13, the curvilinear trapezoids are shaded; in each case, the trapezoid is bounded by the x-axis, the vertical lines $x = a$ and $x = b$, and the curve. One can easily compute their areas if $k = 0$ or $k = 1$.

In fact, if $k = 0$, the area of $ACDB$ is

$$\overline{CD} \cdot \overline{AC} = (b - a) \cdot 1 = b - a,$$

which can be written in the form

$$\frac{b^1 - a^1}{1}.$$

If $k = 1$, the area of $ACDB$ is

$$\overline{CD} \cdot \frac{\overline{AC} + \overline{BD}}{2} = (b - a)\frac{a + b}{2} = \frac{b^2 - a^2}{2}.$$

And as we shall see in succeeding sections, if $k = 2$, the area of $ACDB$ is $\dfrac{b^3 - a^3}{3}$; if $k = 3$, the area is $\dfrac{b^4 - a^4}{4}$; and in general, when k is a nonnegative integer, the area of the corresponding curvilinear trapezoid is $\dfrac{b^{k+1} - a^{k+1}}{k + 1}$. Obviously this general result embraces all the above special cases.

4. CALCULATION OF APPROXIMATE AREA OF *ABCD*

For simplicity, let us take a definite value for the exponent k, for example, $k = 5$. In addition, let us assume that $0 < a < b$. We shall examine the graph of the function $y = x^5$ and, following the method outlined in section 2, prove that the area of the curvilinear trapezoid $ACDB$ (see Fig. 14 on page 8) is

$$\frac{b^6 - a^6}{6}.$$

We must compute the sum of the areas of a very large number of rectangles—pieces of the step-like figure (Fig. 14). To simplify the calculation, let us choose the rectangles so that their areas form a geometric progression. To do this, we take the points E, F, G, H, ..., I on the x-axis so that the lengths $\overline{OC} = a$, $\overline{OE}$, $\overline{OF}$, $\overline{OG}$, $\overline{OI}$, $\overline{OD} = b$ form a geometric progression. Let us denote the number of terms in this progression by $n + 1$, and its common ratio by q (since $b > a$, $q > 1$). Then we obtain the equalities:

$$\overline{OC} = a, \quad \overline{OE} = aq, \quad \overline{OF} = aq^2, \quad \overline{OG} = aq^3, \quad \ldots,$$
$$\overline{OI} = aq^{n-1} \quad \overline{OD} = aq^n = b.$$

In Fig. 14, only 6 rectangles are drawn, and hence $n + 1 = 7$, but we shall assume that n is any arbitrarily large number, for example, $n = 1000, 10,000, 100,000$, etc.

The bases of the rectangles form a geometric progression with the same common ratio q:

$$\overline{CE} = \overline{OE} - \overline{OC} = a(q - 1),$$
$$\overline{EF} = \overline{OF} - \overline{OE} = aq(q - 1),$$
$$\overline{FG} = \overline{OG} - \overline{OF} = aq^2(q - 1),$$

. . . .

$$\overline{ID} = \overline{OD} - \overline{OI} = aq^{n-1}(q - 1).$$

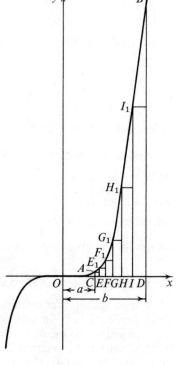

Fig. 14

(The number of terms in this progression and the next is n, not $n + 1$.)

The altitudes of the rectangles are the segments CA, EE_1, FF_1, $GG_1, \ldots, II_1$; each has length equal to the fifth power of its abscissa (because we are working with the function $y = x^5$). Consequently,

$$\overline{CA} = \overline{OC}^5 = a^5,$$
$$\overline{EE_1} = \overline{OE}^5 = a^5q^5,$$
$$\overline{FF_1} = \overline{OF}^5 = a^5q^{10},$$
$$\overline{GG_1} = \overline{OG}^5 = a^5q^{15},$$

. . . .

$$\overline{II_1} = \overline{OI}^5 = a^5q^{5(n-1)}.$$

We see that the altitudes of the rectangles also form a geometric progression with ratio $q^5 (= q^k)$.

Since the bases of the rectangles form a geometric progression with ratio q, and the altitudes a geometric progression with ratio $q^5 (= q^k)$, the areas of the rectangles ought to form a geometric progression with ratio $q \cdot q^5 = q^6 (= q^{k+1})$:

$$\overline{CE} \cdot \overline{CA} = a(q - 1)a^5 = a^6(q - 1),$$
$$\overline{EF} \cdot \overline{EE_1} = aq(q - 1)a^5q^5 = a^6q^6(q - 1),$$
$$\overline{FG} \cdot \overline{FF_1} = aq^2(q - 1)a^5q^{10} = a^6q^{12}(q - 1),$$

. . . .

$$\overline{ID} \cdot \overline{II_1} = aq^{n-1}(q - 1)a^5q^{5(n-1)} = a^6q^{6(n-1)}(q - 1).$$

Hence the sum of the areas of the rectangles, which is the area of the step-like figure, is the sum of the geometric progression with first term $a^6(q - 1)$, last term $a^6 q^{6(n-1)}(q - 1)$, and ratio q^6:

$$\frac{a^6 q^{6(n-1)}(q - 1)q^6 - a^6(q - 1)}{q^6 - 1} = [(aq^n)^6 - a^6]\frac{q - 1}{q^6 - 1}$$

$$= \frac{b^6 - a^6}{q^5 + q^4 + q^3 + q^2 + q + 1}$$

(where we have used

$$b = aq^n \quad \text{and} \quad \frac{q^6 - 1}{q - 1} = q^5 + q^4 + q^3 + q^2 + q + 1).$$

5. PASSING TO THE LIMIT TO OBTAIN THE AREA OF **ABCD**

Let us increase the number n of rectangles indefinitely. Since the bases of the rectangles form an increasing geometric progression ($q > 1$), the first of these bases is smaller than each of the rest. But the sum of the lengths of all n bases is $b - a$; consequently $\overline{CE}$ is less than $\frac{b - a}{n}$, that is,

$$aq - a < \frac{b - a}{n}, \quad \text{whence} \quad q - 1 < \frac{b - a}{na}.$$

The right side of the last inequality approaches zero as n increases; since the left side is positive, it must also approach zero, that is, q approaches 1.

Hence it follows that q^2, q^3, q^4, and q^5 also approach 1, and the sum

$$q^5 + q^4 + q^3 + q^2 + q + 1$$

approaches

$$1 + 1 + 1 + 1 + 1 + 1 = 6;$$

consequently, the total area of the step-like figure, which is

$$\frac{b^6 - a^6}{q^5 + q^4 + q^3 + q^2 + q + 1},$$

approaches as its limit

$$\frac{b^6 - a^6}{6}.$$

The required area of the curvilinear trapezoid must be equal to this limit:

$$S = \frac{b^6 - a^6}{6}.$$

6. GENERALIZATION OF THE PREVIOUS CASE

In the preceding section the result was obtained for $k = 5$. If we carried out the same operations for any natural number k, we would obtain

$$S = \frac{b^{k+1} - a^{k+1}}{k + 1}$$

as the formula for the area, S, of a curvilinear trapezoid, bounded by the graph of the function $y = x^k$, the x-axis, and the two straight lines $x = a$, $x = b$.

Also, the results of the preceding section were obtained by assuming $0 < a < b$, that is, that the curvilinear trapezoid lies to the right of the y-axis. If $a < b < 0$, the proof is carried out in the same manner. However, taking the ratio of the progression q, as before, to be positive and greater than 1, we must now consider b as the first term of the progression, and a as the last (since $|a| > |b|$). Repeating the operations, we arrive at the same result:

$$S = \frac{b^{k+1} - a^{k+1}}{k + 1}.$$

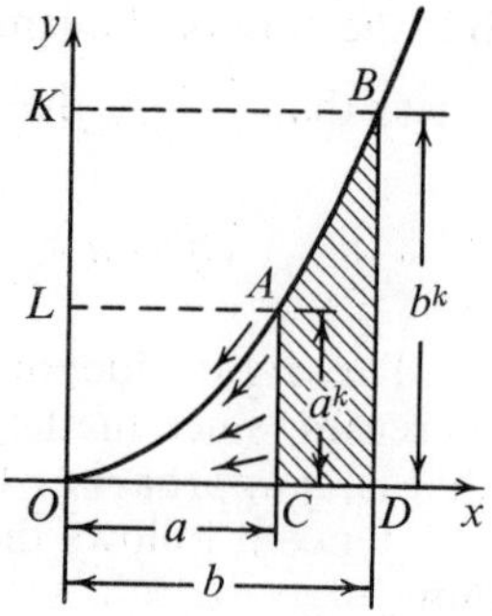

If k is an odd number, then $k + 1$ is even; hence, b^{k+1} and a^{k+1} are positive numbers, and the first is smaller than the second. Hence, in this case S is negative. This is just as it should be, because for k odd the corresponding curvilinear trapezoid lies below the x-axis (see the left parts of Fig. 11 and 13).

Fig. 15

Let us return to the case $0 < a < b$. If we leave b constant and let a approach zero, then the curvilinear trapezoid will be extended to the left, and for $a = 0$ will become a curvilinear triangle ODB (Fig. 15) (assuming $k \geq 1$). Obviously, as a approaches zero, the area of the curvilinear trapezoid will approach the area of a curvilinear triangle. Indeed, the difference between the area of the curvilinear triangle and the area of the curvilinear trapezoid will be less than the area of the rectangle $OCAL$, which also approaches zero. On the other hand, as a approaches zero, the area of the curvilinear trapezoid (as is seen from the derived formula) approaches $\frac{b^{k+1}}{k + 1}$. Therefore the area of the curvilinear triangle ODB is $\frac{b^{k+1}}{k + 1}$, which is $\frac{1}{k + 1}$ times the area of the rectangle *ODBK,* or $\dfrac{2}{k+1}$ times the area of a right triangle with the same legs. For $k = 1$ we obtain the function $y = x$, the graph of which is a straight line (see Fig. 9). The triangle then becomes an ordinary right triangle, and its area is $\dfrac{1}{1+1} = \dfrac{1}{2}$ times the product of the legs.

We obtain analogous results in the case $a < b < 0$, that is, when the curvilinear trapezoid lies at the left of the y-axis. Then, leaving a constant, we let b approach zero; the expression $\dfrac{b^{k+1} - a^{k+1}}{k+1}$ approaches the limit $-\dfrac{a^{k+1}}{k+1}$, which is the area of the corresponding curvilinear triangle.

We can consider the curvilinear triangle as a special case of the curvilinear trapezoid. From what has been demonstrated here, it follows that the formula

$$S = \frac{b^{k+1} - a^{k+1}}{k+1}$$

is also valid for curvilinear triangles. To apply it, we need only set $a = 0$ (if the triangle is to the right of the y-axis) or $b = 0$ (if the triangle is to the left of the y-axis).

2. Integrals

7. THE INTEGRAL

Let us return to the general problem—calculating areas of curvilinear trapezoids. Let $ACDB$ be the curvilinear trapezoid bounded by the arc AB of the graph of the function $y = f(x)$, the two perpendiculars AC and BD dropped from the ends of the arc to the x-axis, and the segment CD on the x-axis cut off by these perpendiculars (Fig. 16). If $\overline{OC} = a$, and $\overline{OD} = b$, and $a < b$, then the area of $ACDB$ is denoted thus:

$$\int_a^b f(x)\ dx. \tag{*}$$

Every detail of this expression has a definite meaning. The function $f(x)$, whose graph bounds one side of the curvilinear trapezoid is indicated, as are the numbers a and b which fix the left and right boundaries. The expression (*) is also meant to remind one of the method of calculating the area of $ACDB$; this method, set forth in sections 2 and 3, consists of the calculation of the sum of the areas of the rectangles which form the step-like figure, and the passage to the limit. The sign $\int$ represents a lengthened letter S —the first letter of the Latin word *summa*—sum. The letter S is written in this unusual manner to remind us that the computation of the area of a curvilinear

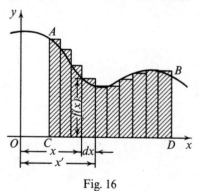

Fig. 16

trapezoid is not only the computation of a sum but also the passage to a limit. On the right of the symbol $\int$, called the *integral sign* (from the Latin *integer*—whole, complete), we see the product $f(x)\ dx$. It represents the area of a rectangle with altitude $f(x)$ and base dx. The letter d, standing in front of x is the initial

12

letter of the Latin word *differentia*—difference; dx denotes the difference of the two values of x (see Fig. 16): $dx = x' - x$. The number a is called the lower limit, and b the upper limit of integration. (Here the word "limit" is used in the sense of "boundary.")

Thus, the expression (*) gives us full information concerning the shape and dimensions of the curvilinear trapezoid (the numbers a and b and the function $f(x)$ do this), while reminding us of the manner of determining its area by calculating the areas of the rectangles with altitude $f(x)$ and base dx, summing these areas, and then passing to the limit. (The integral sign reminds us of the operations of summation and passage to the limit.) The expression (*) is read: "The integral from a to b of f of x dx." We repeat that this expression represents the area of the curvilinear trapezoid $ACDB$. Using our new notation, we can state the results of section 6 in the following manner:

$$\int_a^b x^k \, dx = \frac{b^{k+1} - a^{k+1}}{k + 1}$$

k being a nonnegative integer. This is read: "The integral from a to b of $x^k \, dx$ is equal to the difference between b^{k+1} and a^{k+1} divided by $(k + 1)$."

8. PROPERTIES OF INTEGRALS

Let us discuss several simple properties of integrals. It is obvious that the area of $ACDB$ added to the area of $BDD'B'$ gives the area of $ACD'B'$ (Fig. 17). The first is equal to $\int_a^b f(x) \, dx$, the second to $\int_b^c f(x) \, dx$, and the third to $\int_a^c f(x) \, dx$. Consequently we have:

$$\int_a^b f(x) \, dx + \int_b^c f(x) \, dx = \int_a^c f(x) \, dx.$$

Here we are assuming that $a < b < c$; if, on the other hand, $a < c < b$ (Fig. 18), then, noting that the area of $ACD'B'$ added to the area of $B'D'DB$ gives the area of $ACDB$, we obtain:

$$\int_a^c f(x) \, dx + \int_c^b f(x) \, dx = \int_a^b f(x) \, dx.$$

In introducing in section 7 the concept of the integral $\int_a^b f(x) \, dx$, we assumed that $a < b$, that is, that the lower limit was less than the upper limit. For this very reason, the notation for the area of

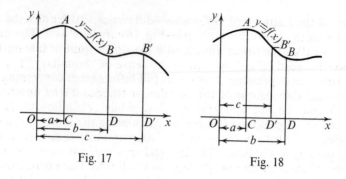

Fig. 17   Fig. 18

$BDD'B'$, where $\overline{OD} = b$ and $\overline{OD'} = c$, for $b < c$ (Fig. 17) was written in the form $\int_b^c f(x)\,dx$, and for $b > c$ (Fig. 18) in the form $\int_c^b f(x)\,dx$. (In each case the lower limit is less than the upper.) In the first case the difference $\int_a^c f(x)\,dx - \int_a^b f(x)\,dx$ was equal to $\int_b^c f(x)\,dx$, and in the second it was equal to $-\int_c^b f(x)\,dx$. (Here we have used the two above equalities.) In order to incorporate both cases into one formula, let us agree for $b > c$ to use the notation:

$$\int_b^c f(x)\,dx = - \int_c^b f(x)\,dx.$$

In other words, we now also recognize an integral in which the lower limit is greater than the upper and understand it to be the negative of the area of the associated curvilinear trapezoid. Then instead of two different formulas:

$$\int_a^c f(x)\,dx - \int_a^b f(x)\,dx = \int_b^c f(x)\,dx \quad (b < c)$$

and

$$\int_a^c f(x)\,dx - \int_a^b f(x)\,dx = - \int_c^b f(x)\,dx \quad (b > c),$$

we write in all cases

$$\int_a^c f(x)\,dx - \int_a^b f(x)\,dx = \int_b^c f(x)\,dx \quad (b \neq c).$$

14

Since the left side becomes zero when $b = c$, it is natural to define the value of the integral $\int_b^b f(x)\, dx$ to be zero. Geometrically, this means that the area of a figure with width equal to zero is zero.

Now, whether $b < c$, $b > c$, or $b = c$, we can use the formula

$$\int_a^c f(x)\, dx - \int_a^b f(x)\, dx = \int_b^c f(x)\, dx.$$

This formula can be rewritten as follows:

$$\int_a^b f(x)\, dx + \int_b^c f(x)\, dx = \int_a^c f(x)\, dx.$$

We leave it to the reader to verify, using the results of this section, that the formula

$$\int_a^b x^k\, dx = \frac{b^{k+1} - a^{k+1}}{k + 1}$$

is valid for *arbitrary* a and b; that is, the formula holds no matter what values a and b may happen to have (and not just for $0 \le a < b$, or $a < b \le 0$).

9. INTEGRALS OF SUMS AND DIFFERENCES

Let us assume that $f(x)$ is a sum or a difference of two functions: $f(x) = g(x) + h(x)$ or $f(x) = g(x) - h(x)$. (For example, $f(x) = x^3 - x^5$.) Then we can replace the integral of $f(x)$ with the sum or difference of the integrals of the functions $g(x)$ and $h(x)$:

$$\int_a^b f(x)\, dx = \int_a^b g(x)\, dx + \int_a^b h(x)\, dx$$

or

$$\int_a^b f(x)\, dx = \int_a^b g(x)\, dx - \int_a^b h(x)\, dx.$$

For instance,

$$\int_a^b (x^3 - x^5)\, dx = \int_a^b x^3\, dx - \int_a^b x^5\, dx = \frac{b^4 - a^4}{4} - \frac{b^6 - a^6}{6}.$$

15

Let us prove this property of integrals for the case of a sum. Thus, let $f(x) = g(x) + h(x)$; the graphs of the three functions $g(x)$, $h(x)$, and $f(x)$ are depicted in Fig. 19. We must prove that

$$\int_a^b f(x)\, dx = \int_a^b g(x)\, dx + \int_a^b h(x)\, dx,$$

that is, that the area of $ACDB$ is the sum of the areas of $A_1 C_1 D_1 B_1$ and $A_2 C_2 D_2 B_2$. Let us divide the segment of the x-axis between the points $x = a$ and $x = b$ into sections and construct the corresponding step-like figures for all three curvilinear trapezoids represented in Fig. 19. It is obvious that the area of each rectangle in the lowest part of the illustration is equal to the sum of the areas of the two rectangles situated above it in the middle and upper parts. Therefore, the area of the lowest step-like figure is the sum of the areas of the two step-like figures lying above it. This relation between the areas of the step-like figures will hold for an arbitrary division of the segment on the x-axis between $x = a$ and $x = b$. If we divide this segment into an even larger number of parts, whose lengths approach zero, then the area of the lowest figure will approach as its limit

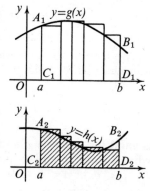

$$\int_a^b f(x)\, dx,$$

and the two figures lying above it, the limits

$$\int_a^b g(x)\, dx \quad \text{and} \quad \int_a^b h(x)\, dx.$$

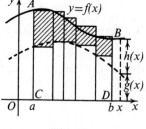

Fig. 19

Because the limit of a sum is equal to the sum of the limits, it follows that

$$\int_a^b f(x)\, dx = \int_a^b [g(x) + h(x)]\, dx = \int_a^b g(x)\, dx + \int_a^b h(x)\, dx.$$

In the same manner, we can prove that

$$\int_a^b [g(x) - h(x)]\, dx = \int_a^b g(x)\, dx - \int_a^b h(x)\, dx.$$

It is easy to see that this property of integrals, just established, is also valid when $f(x)$ is the sum of a larger number of terms. For example, if $f(x) = g(x) - h(x) + k(x)$, then

$$\int_a^b [g(x) - h(x) + k(x)]\, dx = \int_a^b [g(x) - h(x)]\, dx + \int_a^b k(x)\, dx$$

$$= \int_a^b g(x)\, dx - \int_a^b h(x)\, dx + \int_a^b k(x)\, dx.$$

10. THE CALCULATION OF $\int_a^b Cf(x)\, dx$

We shall now examine the relation between the integrals

$$\int_a^b f(x)\, dx \quad \text{and} \quad \int_a^b Cf(x)\, dx,$$

where C is any number (constant); for example, the relation between the integrals $\int_a^b x^3\, dx$ and $\int_a^b 2x^3\, dx$. We shall show that

$$\int_a^b Cf(x)\, dx = C \int_a^b f(x)\, dx;$$

for example,

$$\int_a^b 2x^3\, dx = 2 \int_a^b x^3\, dx = 2 \cdot \frac{b^4 - a^4}{4} = \frac{b^4 - a^4}{2}.$$

For simplicity, let C be some definite number; for example, let $C = \frac{1}{2}$. Let us now compare the integrals

$$\int_a^b f(x)\, dx \quad \text{and} \quad \int_a^b \tfrac{1}{2} f(x)\, dx.$$

In Fig. 20, we draw curvilinear trapezoids whose areas represent these integrals. Let us divide the segment on the x-axis between the points $x = a$ and $x = b$ into an arbitrary number of pieces and

17

construct the corresponding step-like figures. It is easy to see that the area of each rectangle in the lower section of the illustration is equal to half of the area of the corresponding rectangle in the upper section. Therefore, the area of the lower step-like figure is half of the area of the upper step-like figure. Passing to the limit (as in section 9), we conclude that the total area of the lower curvilinear trapezoid is half the area of the upper curvilinear trapezoid:

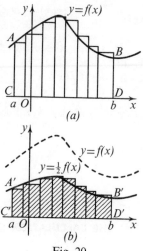

$$\int_a^b \tfrac{1}{2} f(x)\, dx = \tfrac{1}{2} \int_a^b f(x)\, dx.$$

Fig. 20

In this argument we have assumed that the number C is positive; had we taken C to be negative, for example $C = -\dfrac{1}{2}$, then we would have had to replace Fig. 20b by Fig. 21.

Now, when we compare the area of $ACDB$ with the area of $A''C''D''B''$, we find that a change occurs not only in the magnitude of the area, but also in its sign. Consequently,

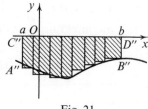

$$\int_a^b (-\tfrac{1}{2}) f(x)\, dx = -\tfrac{1}{2} \int_a^b f(x)\, dx.$$

Fig. 21

Of course, we took $C = \pm\dfrac{1}{2}$ only for the purpose of achieving greater clarity in our reasoning, but the equality

$$\int_a^b C f(x)\, dx = C \int_a^b f(x)\, dx$$

is valid for any number C.

As an example of the application of the properties of integrals proved in this and the previous section, let us compute the integral $\int_0^1 (3x^2 - 2x + 1)\, dx$. We obtain:

18

$$\int_0^1 (3x^2 - 2x + 1)\, dx = \int_0^1 3x^2\, dx - \int_0^1 2x\, dx + \int_0^1 1\, dx$$

$$= 3 \int_0^1 x^2\, dx - 2 \int_0^1 x\, dx + \int_0^1 x^0\, dx$$

$$= 3 \cdot \frac{1^3 - 0^3}{3} - 2 \cdot \frac{1^2 - 0^2}{2} + \frac{1^1 - 0^1}{1}$$

$$= 3 \cdot \frac{1}{3} - 2 \cdot \frac{1}{2} + 1 = 1.$$

11. THE INTEGRAL OF THE FUNCTION $f(x) = \dfrac{1}{x}$

Let us now consider the function defined by

$$y = \frac{1}{x} = x^{-1}.$$

Its graph is called an *equilateral hyperbola;* it is represented in Fig. 22. If we try to apply to this function the formula for the area

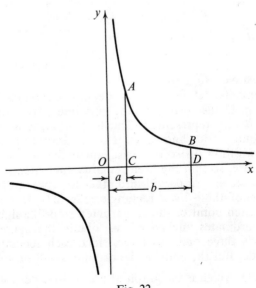

Fig. 22

of a curvilinear trapezoid derived above for $k \geq 0$,

$$\int_a^b x^k \, dx = \frac{b^{k+1} - a^{k+1}}{k + 1},$$

and observe that $k + 1 = 0$ and $b^{k+1} = a^{k+1} = 1$, we obtain on the right-hand side the expression $\frac{0}{0}$, which makes no sense. Therefore, our formula cannot be applied in the case $k = -1$.

The fact that our formula is useless for computing the integral $\int_a^b x^{-1} \, dx$, however, does not prevent us from examining certain of this integral's properties.

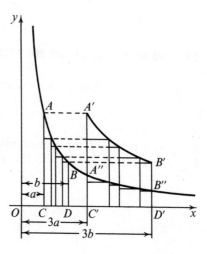

We shall prove that if a and b are each multiplied by the same number $q > 0$, then the new curvilinear trapezoid obtained *has the same area as the original*. In other words, we shall prove that

$$\int_{aq}^{bq} x^{-1} \, dx = \int_a^b x^{-1} \, dx,$$

Fig. 23

for every positive q ($q > 0$).

For simplicity, let us give q a definite numerical value, say $q = 3$. In Fig. 23 the corresponding curvilinear trapezoids $ACDB$ and $A''C'D'B''$ are represented. The first of them is narrow and tall, the second is wide and short. It is necessary to prove that the increase of width in the second case equals the decrease of height in the first case, so that the area remains unchanged. To do this, let us divide the first trapezoid into other narrower trapezoids and replace each of these by a rectangle (Fig. 23). If we triple the abscissa of each point of the constructed step-like figure $ACDB$, leaving the ordinates unchanged, we obtain the figure $A'C'D'B'$, whose area is three times as large, since each rectangle is three times as wide. But the ends of the ordinates will no longer lie on our hyperbola, which is the graph of $y = \frac{1}{x}$. In order for the points to remain on it, it is necessary to decrease the ordinate by the same factor as we increased the abscissa. If we divide all the ordinates of the figure $A'C'D'B'$ by three, then we obtain the figure $A''C'D'B''$. This is a curvilinear trapezoid, bounded above by the arc of the hyperbola $y = \dfrac{1}{x}$, and on the sides by the lines $x = 3a$ and $x = 3b$. The rectangles obtained in this manner have bases three times as wide as the initial rectangles, and altitudes one third as high. Therefore, their areas are the same as the areas of the initial rectangles. Consequently, the areas of the two step-like figures are identical and the corresponding limits are identical as well; that is, for the areas of the curvilinear trapezoids we have:

$$\int_{qa}^{qb} x^{-1} \, dx = \int_{a}^{b} x^{-1} \, dx.$$

We have proved this on the assumption that $a < b$, but the equality is also valid for $a = b$ and for $a > b$. In fact, if $a = b$, then $aq = bq$ and both integrals are equal to zero, so that the equality remains true. On the other hand, if $a > b$, then $aq > bq$; in this case the equality

$$\int_{bq}^{aq} x^{-1} \, dx = \int_{b}^{a} x^{-1} \, dx$$

will be valid (now $b < a$; therefore b and a exchange roles). But in section 8 we agreed that $\int_{a}^{b} f(x) \, dx$ (for $a > b$) denotes $- \int_{b}^{a} f(x) \, dx$. Consequently,

$$\int_{aq}^{bq} x^{-1} \, dx = - \int_{bq}^{aq} x^{-1} \, dx,$$

$$\int_{a}^{b} x^{-1} \, dx = - \int_{b}^{a} x^{-1} \, dx;$$

but since the right sides of these equalities are equal, the left sides must be equal also:

$$\int_{aq}^{bq} x^{-1} \, dx = \int_{a}^{b} x^{-1} \, dx.$$

Thus, the relation we have proved remains valid whether $a < b$, $a = b$, or $a > b$.

3. Logarithms

12. INTRODUCTION TO NATURAL LOGARITHMS

Let us take $a = 1$ and consider $\int_1^b x^{-1}\,dx$. If $b > 1$, then this integral represents the area of a curvilinear trapezoid $ACDB$ (Fig. 24). If $b = 1$, then this integral is zero. Finally, if $0 < b < 1$, then

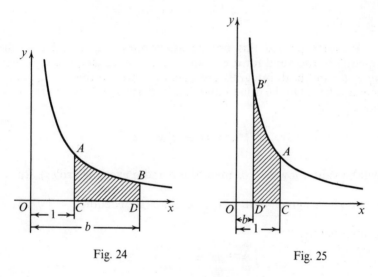

Fig. 24   Fig. 25

the lower limit of the integral is smaller than the upper, and we obtain

$$\int_1^b x^{-1}\,dx = -\int_b^1 x^{-1}\,dx.$$

This means that in this case the integral differs only in sign from the area of the curvilinear trapezoid $B'D'CA$ (Fig. 25). In any case, for any positive number b the integral $\int_1^b x^{-1}\,dx$ has a well-defined value. It is positive when $b > 1$, zero when $b = 1$, and negative when $b < 1$.

It is obvious that the integral $\int_1^b x^{-1}\,dx$ is a function of b. This function plays an important role in mathematics; it is called the *natural logarithm* of the number b and is denoted by "ln b." Here "l" and "n" are the first letters of the Latin words for logarithm (*logarithmus*) and natural (*naturalis*). Thus

$$\int_1^b x^{-1}\,dx = \ln b.$$

Let us mention some properties of natural logarithms. First of all:

$$\ln b > 0, \text{ if } b > 1;$$
$$\ln 1 = 0;$$
$$\ln b < 0, \text{ if } 0 < b < 1.$$

Let us now deduce the following fundamental property of logarithms: *The logarithm of the product of two numbers is equal to the sum of their logarithms* (for example, ln $6 = $ ln $2 + $ ln 3). In general:

$$\ln (bc) = \ln b + \ln c,$$

i.e.,

$$\int_1^{bc} x^{-1}\,dx = \int_1^b x^{-1}\,dx + \int_1^c x^{-1}\,dx.$$

Indeed, as has been shown previously (section 11):

$$\int_1^c x^{-1}\,dx = \int_q^{qc} x^{-1}\,dx$$

for any $q > 0$. Let us take $q = b$; then we obtain:

$$\int_1^c x^{-1}\,dx = \int_b^{bc} x^{-1}\,dx.$$

Therefore,

$$\int_1^b x^{-1}\,dx + \int_1^c x^{-1}\,dx = \int_1^b x^{-1}\,dx + \int_b^{bc} x^{-1}\,dx;$$

but this last sum, according to the results obtained in section 8, can be replaced by the integral $\int_1^{bc} x^{-1}\,dx$. Thus,

$$\int_1^b x^{-1}\,dx + \int_1^c x^{-1}\,dx = \int_1^{bc} x^{-1}\,dx.$$

From this property we can deduce certain corollaries. Take $b > 0$; then, according to what has been proved,

$$\ln 1 = \ln \left(b \cdot \frac{1}{b} \right) = \ln b + \ln \frac{1}{b},$$

and since $\ln 1 = 0$, $\ln b + \ln \frac{1}{b} = 0$; hence,

$$\ln \frac{1}{b} = -\ln b.$$

For example, $\ln \frac{1}{2} = -\ln 2$. Furthermore, if $b > 0$ and $c > 0$, then

$$\ln \frac{c}{b} = \ln \left(c \cdot \frac{1}{b} \right) = \ln c + \ln \frac{1}{b},$$

whence

$$\ln \frac{c}{b} = \ln c - \ln b;$$

in other words, *the logarithm of a quotient is equal to the logarithm of the dividend minus the logarithm of the divisor.*

We have formulated the fundamental property of the logarithm of a product of two factors, but it is also valid for a product of any number of factors. Thus, for example, if there are three factors, we obtain:

$$\ln (bcd) = \ln [(bc)d] = \ln (bc) + \ln d$$
$$= (\ln b + \ln c) + \ln d = \ln b + \ln c + \ln d.$$

It is obvious that no matter how many factors there are, the logarithm of their product is always equal to the sum of their logarithms.

Let us apply this result to the logarithm of b^k, where the exponent is a positive integer k. We see that

$$\ln b^k = \underbrace{\ln (bb \cdots b)}_{k \text{ times}} = \underbrace{\ln b + \ln b + \cdots + \ln b}_{k \text{ times}} = k \cdot \ln b.$$

For example, $\ln 16 = \ln 2^4 = 4 \cdot \ln 2$.

Let $c = \sqrt[k]{b}$; then $c^k = b$ and, consequently,

$$\ln b = \ln c^k = k \cdot \ln c = k \cdot \ln \sqrt[k]{b},$$

whence
$$\ln \sqrt[k]{b} = \frac{1}{k} \cdot \ln b.$$

For example,
$$\ln \sqrt[3]{2} = \frac{1}{3} \cdot \ln 2.$$

If $c = b^{\frac{p}{q}}$, where p and q are positive whole numbers, then on the basis of our previous results we obtain:

$$\ln b^{\frac{p}{q}} = \ln \sqrt[q]{b^p} = \frac{1}{q} \cdot \ln b^p = \frac{1}{q} \cdot p \cdot \ln b = \frac{p}{q} \cdot \ln b.$$

Consequently, the equation
$$\ln b^k = k \cdot \ln b$$

holds not only when k is a positive integer, but also when k is a fraction of the form $\frac{p}{q}$, where p and q are positive integers.

It is easy to see that this same equation also holds for k negative (an integer or fraction). Indeed, if $k < 0$, then $-k > 0$, and we have:

$$\ln b^k = \ln \frac{1}{b^{-k}} = -\ln b^{-k} = -(-k \cdot \ln b) = k \cdot \ln b.$$

Finally, this property also holds for $k = 0$:

$$\ln b^0 = \ln 1 = 0 = 0 \cdot \ln b.$$

Thus, we can state that *for any rational number k, we have*

$$\ln b^k = k \cdot \ln b.$$

One can even prove that this relation holds for irrational k; for example,

$$\ln b^{\sqrt{2}} = \sqrt{2} \cdot \ln b.$$

However, let us accept this last statement without proof and hereafter make free use of the property

$$\mathbf{\ln\, b^k = k \cdot \ln\, b}$$

for all values of the exponent k, rational or irrational.

25

13. INTRODUCTION TO THE COMPUTATION OF LOGARITHMS

Let us turn to the computation of logarithms. We shall compute ln 2, that is, the area of the curvilinear trapezoid $ACDB$, represented in Fig. 26a. Let us divide the segment CD into 10 equal parts and draw the corresponding segments; $K_1L_1, K_2L_2, \ldots, K_9L_9$. In order to find the best possible approximation of ln 2, let us replace each

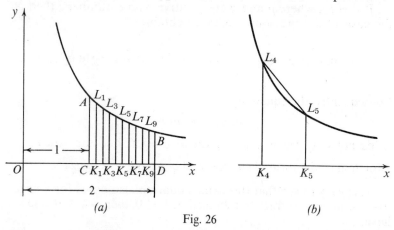

Fig. 26

of the ten resulting narrow curvilinear trapezoids, not by a rectangle, as we did previously, but by an ordinary trapezoid. To do this, let us join with straight line segments the points A and L_1, L_1 and $L_2, \ldots, L_9$ and B. In Fig. 26a, it would be hard to distinguish the ordinary trapezoids from the curvilinear ones; in order to see the difference between them more readily, we show an enlargement in Fig. 26b. The area of each trapezoid is half the product of its altitude and the sum of its bases. But in our case all altitudes are the same:

$$\overline{CK_1} = \overline{K_1K_2} = \cdots = \overline{K_9D} = 0.1.$$

Consequently, the areas of the trapezoids will be:

$$\frac{\overline{AC} + \overline{K_1L_1}}{2} \cdot 0.1; \quad \frac{\overline{K_1L_1} + \overline{K_2L_2}}{2} \cdot 0.1; \ldots;$$

$$\frac{\overline{K_9L_9} + \overline{BD}}{2} \cdot 0.1;$$

the sum of all these areas is

$$0.1 \cdot \frac{(\overline{AC} + \overline{K_1L_1}) + (\overline{K_1L_1} + \overline{K_2L_2}) + \cdots (\overline{K_9L_9} + \overline{BD})}{2}$$

26

or $0.1(0.5\overline{AC} + \overline{K_1L_1} + \overline{K_2L_2} + \cdots + \overline{K_9L_9} + 0.5\overline{BD})$.

It remains to observe that the lengths of all of the bases of the trapezoids are equal to ordinates of points on the graph of the function $y = \dfrac{1}{x}$, with the following corresponding abscissas:

$$1, 1.1, 1.2, 1.3, 1.4, 1.5, 1.6, 1.7, 1.8, 1.9, 2.$$

Therefore,

$$\overline{AC} = \frac{1}{1} = 1.000, \qquad \overline{K_1L_1} = \frac{1}{1.1} = 0.909,$$

$$\overline{K_2L_2} = \frac{1}{1.2} = 0.833, \qquad \overline{K_3L_3} = \frac{1}{1.3} = 0.769,$$

$$\overline{K_4L_4} = \frac{1}{1.4} = 0.714, \qquad \overline{K_5L_5} = \frac{1}{1.5} = 0.667,$$

$$\overline{K_6L_6} = \frac{1}{1.6} = 0.625, \qquad \overline{K_7L_7} = \frac{1}{1.7} = 0.588,$$

$$\overline{K_8L_8} = \frac{1}{1.8} = 0.556, \qquad \overline{K_9L_9} = \frac{1}{1.9} = 0.526,$$

$$\overline{BD} = \frac{1}{2} = 0.500.$$

Hence, the sum of the areas of the trapezoids is:

$$0.1(0.500 + 0.909 + 0.833 + 0.769 + 0.714 + 0.667$$
$$+ \ 0.625 + 0.588 + 0.556 + 0.526 + 0.250) = 0.6937.$$

If we examine Fig. 26a, it becomes clear that the sum of the areas of these trapezoids gives a number somewhat greater than the area of the curvilinear trapezoid. This means that we have found an approximation to the value of ln 2 with an excess, that is, that ln 2 is somewhat smaller than 0.6937.

In what follows we shall learn other methods of computing logarithms, which will enable us to compute ln 2 with greater accuracy.

14. APPROXIMATION FORMULAS FOR COMPUTING LOGARITHMS

If one measures abscissas, not from the point O, but from the point C (Fig. 27) and denotes the new abscissas by the letter t, then the relation between the old and new abscissas of the same point will be as follows: $x = 1 + t.$

This relation is valid for any point if we agree that $t > 0$ when $x > 1$, and $t \leq 0$ when $x \leq 1$. By substituting $1 + t$ for x, the function $y = \dfrac{1}{x}$ assumes a different form: $y = \dfrac{1}{1 + t}$, but its graph remains the same. The change which occurs with the introduction of t consists only in a new origin of the coordinate system (C in place of O), and hence, a new y-axis Cy (parallel to the previous one); the curve remains unchanged.

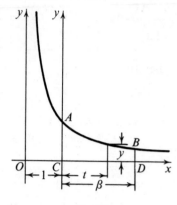

Fig. 27

The area of $ACDB$ also remains unchanged, of course. But when x was the abscissa, this area was represented by the integral

$$\int_1^{1+\beta} x^{-1}\, dx = \ln(1 + \beta),$$

where $\beta = \overline{CD}$. Now, however, when we consider t as the abscissa, the same area is represented by the integral $\int_0^{\beta}(1 + t)^{-1}\, dt$. Comparing the two integrals, we obtain:

$$\ln(1 + \beta) = \int_0^{\beta}(1 + t)^{-1}\, dt.$$

Let us recall the following identity:

$$1 - t + t^2 - t^3 + \cdots - t^{2n-1} = \frac{1 - t^{2n}}{1 + t},$$

which is true because the left side is a geometric progression whose first term is 1, whose common ratio is $-t$, and whose last term is $-t^{2n-1}$. From the above identity it follows that

$$\frac{1}{1 + t} = 1 - t + t^2 - t^3 + \cdots - t^{2n-1} + \frac{t^{2n}}{1 + t}.$$

28

Consequently,

$$\ln{(1+\beta)} = \int_0^\beta \left(1 - t + t^2 - t^3 + \cdots - t^{2n-1} + \frac{t^{2n}}{1+t}\right) dt.$$

We now have under the integral sign in place of $(1+t)^{-1}$ a more complicated and cumbersome expression—a sum of several terms. We know already that the integral of a sum or a difference of functions equals the sum or difference of the integrals of these functions. Consequently,

$$\ln{(1+\beta)} = \int_0^\beta 1 \, dt - \int_0^\beta t \, dt + \int_0^\beta t^2 \, dt - \int_0^\beta t^3 \, dt$$

$$+ \cdots - \int_0^\beta t^{2n-1} \, dt + \int_0^\beta \frac{t^{2n}}{1+t} dt.$$

We know how to compute (section 7) each of the integrals on the right side of this equality with the exception of the last. To be explicit:

$$\int_0^\beta 1 \, dt = \beta, \quad \int_0^\beta t \, dt = \frac{\beta^2}{2}, \quad \int_0^\beta t^2 \, dt = \frac{\beta^3}{3},$$

$$\int_0^\beta t^3 \, dt = \frac{\beta^4}{2}, \ldots, \quad \int_0^\beta t^{2n-1} \, dt = \frac{\beta^{2n}}{2n},$$

from which it follows that

$$\ln{(1+\beta)} = \left(\beta - \frac{\beta^2}{2} + \frac{\beta^3}{3} - \frac{\beta^4}{4} + \cdots - \frac{\beta^{2n}}{2n}\right) + \int_0^\beta \frac{t^{2n}}{1+t} dt.$$

The expression in parentheses on the right side of the latter equality is a polynomial of degree $2n$, arranged according to increasing powers of β. If the value of β is known and if, moreover, a positive whole number n is chosen (we can choose it arbitrarily), then we can easily compute the value of this polynomial. Only the integral $\int_0^\beta \frac{t^{2n}}{1+t} dt$ is difficult to compute. We shall prove in sections 15 and 16 that for $-1 < \beta \le 1$ we can make this integral arbitrarily small, by taking a sufficiently large value for n. In that case we can neglect the last integral completely in computing $\ln (1 + \beta)$, with only a negligible error resulting. Consequently, we obtain the approximation:

$$\ln (1 + \beta) \approx \beta - \frac{\beta^2}{2} + \frac{\beta^3}{3} - \frac{\beta^4}{4} + \cdots - \frac{\beta^{2n}}{2n}.$$

15. AN ESTIMATE OF THE ERROR FOR $0 < \beta \leq 1$

In order to estimate the error which results from using the approximation given above, it is necessary to consider the discarded

integral $\int_0^\beta \frac{t^{2n}}{1 + t} dt$. To begin with, let us assume that $0 < \beta \leq 1$.

Then within the limits of the integration, t remains positive, and consequently

$$0 < \frac{t^{2n}}{1 + t} < t^{2n}.$$

This means that the graph of the function $y = \frac{t^{2n}}{1 + t}$ lies below the graph of the function $y = t^{2n}$ (Fig. 28); therefore, the area of CBA_1 is smaller than the area of CBA, that is,

$$\int_0^\beta \frac{t^{2n}}{1 + t} dt < \int_0^\beta t^{2n} dt = \frac{\beta^{2n+1}}{2n + 1}.$$

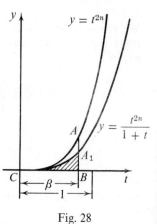

Fig. 28

Thus, the approximation

$$\ln (1 + \beta) \approx \beta - \frac{\beta^2}{2} + \frac{\beta^3}{3} - \frac{\beta^4}{4} + \cdots - \frac{\beta^{2n}}{2n}$$

is valid for $0 < \beta \leq 1$ with an error less than

$$\frac{\beta^{2n+1}}{2n + 1}.$$

Since $0 < \beta \leq 1$, we can make this error as small as we wish by taking n sufficiently large.

However, if we take $\beta = 1$, then the formula derived in section 14 gives us:

$$\ln 2 \approx 1 - \frac{1}{2} + \frac{1}{3} - \frac{1}{4} + \frac{1}{5} - \frac{1}{6} + \cdots + \frac{1}{2n - 1} - \frac{1}{2n},$$

with an error less than $\dfrac{1}{2n + 1}$. If we want to compute $\ln 2$ by this method with an accuracy of 0.001, then it is necessary that $\dfrac{1}{2n + 1} < 0.001$, i.e., $2n + 1 > 1000$; this requirement can be satisfied by taking $2n = 1000$. But this means that on the left side of the equality 1000 terms will appear, whose sum it is necessary to compute. Such work is, of course, excessive; we shall see in succeeding sections several refinements which can be made to reduce the amount of computation.

16. AN ESTIMATE OF THE ERROR FOR $-1 < \beta \leq 0$

Let us turn again to the integral $\int_0^\beta \frac{t^{2n}}{1 + t}\, dt$, but this time let us examine the case where $-1 < \beta \leq 0$. We know that

$$\int_0^\beta \frac{t^{2n}}{1 + t}\, dt = -\int_\beta^0 \frac{t^{2n}}{1 + t}\, dt.$$

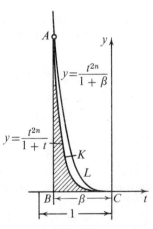

The integral $\int_\beta^0 \frac{t^{2n}}{1 + t}\, dt$ is equal to the area of the figure $ABCK$, shaded in Fig. 29. This figure lies above Ct, since $y = \frac{t^{2n}}{1 + t} > 0$ for $t > -1$. Therefore, the area of $ABCK$ is positive; that is, the integral $\int_\beta^0 \frac{t^{2n}}{1 + t}\, dt$ is a positive number.

It differs from the integral $\int_0^\beta \frac{t^{2n}}{1 + t}\, dt$ only in sign and, consequently, is equal to the latter in absolute value:

$$\int_\beta^0 \frac{t^{2n}}{1 + t}\, dt = \left| \int_0^\beta \frac{t^{2n}}{1 + t}\, dt \right|.$$

Fig. 29

39

Let us also note that for $t > \beta$ and $\beta > -1$, the following inequality holds:

$$1 + t > 1 + \beta > 0;$$

consequently,

$$\frac{1}{1 + t} < \frac{1}{1 + \beta} \qquad \text{and} \qquad \frac{t^{2n}}{1 + t} < \frac{t^{2n}}{1 + \beta}.$$

This means that the graph of the function $y = \dfrac{t^{2n}}{1 + t}$ lies below the graph of the function $y = \dfrac{t^{2n}}{1 + \beta}$ in the interval $\beta < t < 0$ (Fig. 29). Therefore, the area of $ABCK$ is smaller than the area of $ABCL$:

$$\int_\beta^0 \frac{t^{2n}}{1 + t}\, dt < \int_\beta^0 \frac{t^{2n}}{1 + \beta}\, dt.$$

It is easy to compute the right side of the above inequality:

$$\int_\beta^0 \frac{1}{1 + \beta} t^{2n}\, dt = \frac{1}{1 + \beta} \int_\beta^0 t^{2n}\, dt = \frac{1}{1 + \beta} \cdot \frac{0^{2n+1} - \beta^{2n+1}}{2n + 1}$$

$$= -\frac{\beta^{2n+1}}{(2n + 1)(1 + \beta)}.$$

(This is a positive number, since $\beta^{2n+1} < 0$, $1 + \beta > 0$ and $2n + 1 > 0$.) Consequently,

$$\left| \int_0^\beta \frac{t^{2n}}{1 + t}\, dt \right| = \int_\beta^0 \frac{t^{2n}}{1 + t}\, dt < -\frac{\beta^{2n+1}}{(2n + 1)(1 + \beta)}.$$

Therefore, by omitting the term $\displaystyle\int_0^\beta \frac{t^{2n}}{1 + t}\, dt$ in the expression for $\ln(1 + \beta)$, we obtain an error smaller in absolute value than the expression $-\dfrac{\beta^{2n+1}}{(2n + 1)(1 + \beta)}$ $(-1 < \beta \le 0)$. This error approaches zero as n becomes arbitrarily large. Thus, the approximation

$$\ln(1 + \beta) \approx \beta - \frac{\beta^2}{2} + \frac{\beta^3}{3} - \frac{\beta^4}{4} + \cdots - \frac{\beta^{2n}}{2n}$$

is valid for $-1 \le \beta < 0$ with an error no greater than

$$-\frac{\beta^{2n+1}}{(2n + 1)(1 + \beta)}.$$

For example, let us take $\beta = -\frac{1}{2}$; then the error of the approximation will be less than

$$\frac{\dfrac{1}{2^{2n+1}}}{\dfrac{1}{2}(2n+1)} = \frac{1}{(2n+1)2^{2n}}.$$

If we take $n = 4$, then the last fraction will equal $\dfrac{1}{9 \cdot 2^8} = \dfrac{1}{9(256)}$ $= \dfrac{1}{2304} < 0.0005$. Consequently, with this degree of accuracy, we can write:

$$\ln \frac{1}{2} \approx -\frac{1}{2} - \frac{1}{2^2 \cdot 2} - \frac{1}{2^3 \cdot 3} - \frac{1}{2^4 \cdot 4}$$
$$- \frac{1}{2^5 \cdot 5} - \frac{1}{2^6 \cdot 6} - \frac{1}{2^7 \cdot 7} - \frac{1}{2^8 \cdot 8}.$$

Let us perform the computation:

$$\frac{1}{2} = 0.5000, \qquad \frac{1}{2^2 \cdot 2} = 0.1250, \qquad \frac{1}{2^3 \cdot 3} = 0.0417,$$

$$\frac{1}{2^4 \cdot 4} = 0.0156, \qquad \frac{1}{2^5 \cdot 5} = 0.0062, \qquad \frac{1}{2^6 \cdot 6} = 0.0026,$$

$$\frac{1}{2^7 \cdot 7} = 0.0011, \qquad \frac{1}{2^8 \cdot 8} = 0.0005.$$

We obtain

$$\ln \frac{1}{2} \approx -0.6927 \approx -0.693$$

with an accuracy of 0.001 (taking into account the fact that the formula itself might contain an error up to 0.0005, and in addition that in the conversion of each of the eight terms into a decimal fraction there could arise an error up to 0.00005).

Since $\ln \frac{1}{2} = -\ln 2$, it follows that

$$\ln 2 \approx 0.693$$

with an accuracy of 0.001. We have now obtained this result with considerably less computation than would have been necessary in using the formula given in section 15.

If in the approximation for $\ln (1 + \beta)$ we take $\beta = -\frac{2}{3}$, then in a similar manner we can compute $\ln \frac{1}{3}$, thereby obtaining the value

of $\ln 3 = -\ln \frac{1}{3}$ as well. In general, if we take $\beta = -\frac{k}{k+1}$, we obtain $\ln \left(1 - \frac{k}{k+1}\right) = \ln \frac{1}{k+1}$; therefore, we also have $\ln (k+1)$

$= -\ln \frac{1}{k+1}$. However, this method of computing logarithms is still cumbersome. Thus, for example, if we want to compute $\ln 11$, then by taking $k + 1 = 11$, i.e., $k = 10$, we would have to let $\beta = -\frac{10}{11}$. Then the error of the approximating formula would be smaller than

$$\frac{\left(\frac{10}{11}\right)^{2n+1}}{(2n+1)\left(1 - \frac{10}{11}\right)} = \frac{11}{2n+1}\left(\frac{10}{11}\right)^{2n+1}.$$

We have

$$\frac{10}{11} \approx 0.91; \qquad \left(\frac{10}{11}\right)^2 \approx 0.83; \qquad \left(\frac{10}{11}\right)^4 \approx 0.69;$$

$$\left(\frac{10}{11}\right)^8 \approx 0.48; \qquad \left(\frac{10}{11}\right)^{16} \approx 0.29; \qquad \left(\frac{10}{11}\right)^{32} \approx 0.08;$$

$$\left(\frac{10}{11}\right)^{64} \approx 0.006; \qquad \left(\frac{10}{11}\right)^{65} \approx 0.005.$$

Therefore, by taking $2n + 1 = 65$, we can guarantee that the error of the approximation for computing $\ln \frac{1}{11}$ will be less than $\frac{11}{65} \cdot 0.005 \approx 0.001$. Obviously the work of calculating $\ln \frac{1}{11}$ by this method will be very long, for it will be necessary to compute the sum of 64 terms:

$$-\frac{10}{11} - \frac{1}{2}\left(\frac{10}{11}\right)^2 - \frac{1}{3}\left(\frac{10}{11}\right)^3 - \cdots - \frac{1}{64}\left(\frac{10}{11}\right)^{64}.$$

17. BETTER FORMULA FOR THE COMPUTATION OF NATURAL LOGARITHMS

The conclusions reached regarding the approximating formula for $\ln (1 + \beta)$ force us to seek another formula, requiring fewer operations. Such a formula does, in fact, exist. In order to obtain

it, let us take any positive whole number k and assume $\beta = \dfrac{1}{2k+1}$.
Then we obtain:

$$\ln\left(1 + \frac{1}{2k+1}\right) \approx \frac{1}{2k+1} - \frac{1}{2(2k+1)^2}$$
$$+ \frac{1}{3(2k+1)^3} - \frac{1}{4(2k+1)^4} + \cdots$$
$$+ \frac{1}{(2n-1)(2k+1)^{2n-1}} - \frac{1}{2n(2k+1)^{2n}}.$$

Using the estimate derived in section 15, we see that the error in
the above approximation is less than $\dfrac{1}{(2n+1)(2k+1)^{2n+1}}$.

Now let us take β to be negative and equal to $-\dfrac{1}{2k+1}$; we obtain a second approximation:

$$\ln\left(1 - \frac{1}{2k+1}\right) \approx -\frac{1}{2k+1} - \frac{1}{2(2k+1)^2}$$
$$- \frac{1}{3(2k+1)^3} - \frac{1}{4(2k+1)^4} - \cdots$$
$$- \frac{1}{(2n-1)(2k+1)^{2n-1}} - \frac{1}{2n(2k+1)^{2n}},$$

giving $\ln\left(1 - \dfrac{1}{2k+1}\right)$ with an error less than

$$\frac{\dfrac{1}{(2k+1)^{2n+1}}}{(2n+1)\left(1 - \dfrac{1}{2k+1}\right)} = \frac{2k+1}{2k} \cdot \frac{1}{2n+1} \cdot \frac{1}{(2k+1)^{2n+1}}.$$

(Here we have used the formula derived in section 16 for the error
in approximating $\ln(1+\beta)$ with $\beta = -\dfrac{1}{2k+1}$.)

Let us subtract the second approximation from the first, term by
term. We obtain:

$$\ln\left(1 + \frac{1}{2k+1}\right) - \ln\left(1 - \frac{1}{2k+1}\right) \approx \frac{2}{2k+1} + \frac{2}{3(2k+1)^3}$$
$$+ \frac{2}{5(2k+1)^5} + \cdots + \frac{2}{(2n-1)(2k+1)^{2n-1}}.$$

The error of this approximation does not exceed the sum of the admissible errors in the formulas for $\ln\left(1 + \dfrac{1}{2k+1}\right)$ and $\ln\left(1 - \dfrac{1}{2k+1}\right)$ in absolute value; therefore, it is less than

$$\frac{1}{2n+1} \cdot \frac{1}{(2k+1)^{2n+1}} + \frac{2k+1}{2k} \cdot \frac{1}{2n+1} \cdot \frac{1}{(2k+1)^{2n+1}}$$

$$= \frac{4k+1}{2k} \cdot \frac{1}{2n+1} \cdot \frac{1}{(2k+1)^{2n+1}}$$

$$< \frac{4k+2}{2k} \cdot \frac{1}{2n+1} \cdot \frac{1}{(2k+1)^{2n+1}} = \frac{1}{k(2n+1)(2k+1)^{2n}}.$$

Let us convert the difference of the logarithms, observing that it must equal the logarithm of the quotient. We obtain:

$$\ln\left(1 + \frac{1}{2k+1}\right) - \ln\left(1 - \frac{1}{2k+1}\right) = \ln \frac{1 + \dfrac{1}{2k+1}}{1 - \dfrac{1}{2k+1}}$$

$$= \ln \frac{2k+2}{2k} = \ln \frac{k+1}{k} = \ln(k+1) - \ln k.$$

Thus,

$$\ln(k+1) - \ln k \approx \frac{2}{2k+1} + \frac{2}{3(2k+1)^3}$$

$$+ \frac{2}{5(2k+1)^5} + \cdots + \frac{2}{(2n-1)(2k+1)^{2n-1}}, \quad (*)$$

with an error less than $\dfrac{1}{k} \cdot \dfrac{1}{2n+1} \cdot \dfrac{1}{(2k+1)^{2n}}$.

This is the formula we needed. It permits us to compute $\ln(k+1)$, if $\ln k$ is already known. Making use of the fact that $\ln 1 = 0$ and substituting $k = 1$, we can now find $\ln 2$ with an error less than

$$\frac{1}{2n+1} \cdot \frac{1}{3^{2n}}.$$

Let us take $n = 5$; we can then assert that the error will be less than $\dfrac{1}{11} \cdot \dfrac{1}{3^{10}} = \dfrac{1}{11 \cdot 59049} < 0.000002$. Therefore,

$$\ln 2 = \ln 2 - \ln 1 \approx \frac{2}{3} + \frac{2}{3 \cdot 3^3} + \frac{2}{5 \cdot 3^5} + \frac{2}{7 \cdot 3^7} + \frac{2}{9 \cdot 3^9}$$

with an error less than 0.000002. Converting each of the five fractions into decimal fractions to six decimal places (that is, with an accuracy to 0.0000005) and adding them, we obtain the value of ln 2 with accuracy to $0.000002 + 0.0000005 \cdot 5 < 0.000005$:

$$\ln 2 \approx 0.693146 \approx 0.69315.$$

Let us now substitute $k = 2$ and $n = 3$ in formula (*); we obtain

$$\ln 3 - \ln 2 \approx \frac{2}{5} + \frac{2}{3 \cdot 5^3} + \frac{2}{5 \cdot 5^5} \approx 0.40546$$

with an error less than $\frac{1}{2} \cdot \frac{1}{7} \cdot \frac{1}{5^6} = \frac{1}{14 \cdot 15{,}625} < 0.000005$. Therefore,

$$\ln 3 \approx \ln 2 + 0.40546 \approx 1.09861.$$

Going on, we obtain

$$\ln 4 = 2 \cdot \ln 2 \approx 1.38630.$$

Substituting $k = 4$ and $n = 3$ in formula (*), we obtain:

$$\ln 5 - \ln 4 \approx \frac{2}{9} + \frac{2}{3 \cdot 9^3} + \frac{2}{5 \cdot 9^5} \approx 0.223144 \approx 0.22314$$

with an error less than $\frac{1}{4} \cdot \frac{1}{7} \cdot \frac{1}{9^6} = \frac{1}{28 \cdot 531{,}441} < 0.0000001.$

Therefore,

$$\ln 5 \approx \ln 4 + 0.22314 \approx 1.60944.$$

Now we can also find ln 10:

$$\ln 10 = \ln 5 + \ln 2 \approx 2.30259.$$

Finally, in formula (*), taking $k = 10$ and $n = 2$, we obtain:

$$\ln 11 - \ln 10 \approx \frac{2}{21} + \frac{2}{3 \cdot 21^3} \approx 0.09531$$

with an error of less than $\frac{1}{10} \cdot \frac{1}{5} \cdot \frac{1}{21^4} < 0.0000001.$

Therefore,

$$\ln 11 \approx \ln 10 + 0.09531 \approx 2.39790.$$

These examples are sufficient to show how one can construct a table of natural logarithms. In exactly this way, we can obtain the following table of logarithms of whole numbers from 1 to 100, each entry correct to within 0.0005.

n	$\ln n$	n	$\ln n$	n	$\ln n$	n	$\ln n$	n	$\ln n$
1	0.000	21	3.045	41	3.714	61	4.111	81	4.394
2	0.693	22	3.091	42	3.738	62	4.127	82	4.407
3	1.099	23	3.135	43	3.761	63	4.143	83	4.419
4	1.386	24	3.178	44	3.784	64	4.159	84	4.431
5	1.609	25	3.219	45	3.807	65	4.174	85	4.443
6	1.792	26	3.258	46	3.829	66	4.190	86	4.454
7	1.946	27	3.296	47	3.850	67	4.205	87	4.466
8	2.079	28	3.332	48	3.871	68	4.220	88	4.477
9	2.197	29	3.367	49	3.892	69	4.234	89	4.489
10	2.303	30	3.401	50	3.912	70	4.248	90	4.500
11	2.398	31	3.434	51	3.932	71	4.263	91	4.511
12	2.485	32	3.466	52	3.951	72	4.277	92	4.522
13	2.565	33	3.497	53	3.970	73	4.290	93	4.533
14	2.639	34	3.526	54	3.989	74	4.304	94	4.543
15	2.708	35	3.555	55	4.007	75	4.317	95	4.554
16	2.773	36	3.584	56	4.025	76	4.331	96	4.564
17	2.833	37	3.611	57	4.043	77	4.344	97	4.575
18	2.890	38	3.638	58	4.060	78	4.357	98	4.585
19	2.944	39	3.664	59	4.078	79	4.369	99	4.595
20	2.996	40	3.689	60	4.094	80	4.382	100	4.605

18. COMPUTATION WITH THE HELP OF THE TABLE

We have seen that the logarithm of a product is computed by means of addition, the logarithm of a quotient by means of subtraction, the logarithm of a power by means of multiplication (by the exponent), and the logarithm of a root by means of division (by the degree of the root). Consequently, if we have a table of logarithms, then by using it we can replace multiplication by addition, division by subtraction, raising to a power by multiplication, and extraction of a root by division, that is, in each case by a more simple operation. A second year algebra textbook tells in detail how this is done. Here we limit ourselves to a simple example.

Let us suppose that we wish to compute $c = \sqrt[5]{2}$. Let us use the value computed above of $\ln 2 \approx 0.693$. Dividing it by 5 we obtain: $\ln \sqrt[5]{2} = \frac{1}{5} \cdot \ln 2 \approx 0.139$. It remains to find the number $\sqrt[5]{2}$ by means of its logarithm. Our table is not good enough for this; it contains the logarithms 0.000 (corresponding to the number 1) and 0.693 (corresponding to the number 2); the first is too small, while the second is too large. On the basis of this, we can say only that $1 < \sqrt[5]{2} < 2$. But we can observe that $\ln (10 \sqrt[5]{2}) = \ln 10 + \ln \sqrt[5]{2} \approx 2.303 + 0.139 \approx 2.442$. In our table the closest logarithm smaller than 2.442 is 2.398 ($\approx \ln 11$), the closest one larger is 2.485 ($\approx \ln 12$), therefore $11 < 10 \sqrt[5]{2} < 12$. Observing that 2.442 lies approximately halfway between $\ln 11$ and $\ln 12$ (the arithmetic mean of these numbers is 2.441), we can assert that $10 \sqrt[5]{2} \approx 11.5$, i.e.,

$$\sqrt[5]{2} \approx 1.15.$$

To verify this, we need only observe that

$$\ln (100 \sqrt[5]{2}) = \ln 100 + \ln \sqrt[5]{2} \approx 4.605 + 0.139 = 4.744$$

and

$$\ln 115 = \ln 5 + \ln 23 \approx 1.609 + 3.135 = 4.744.$$

19. THE GRAPH OF THE FUNCTION $f(x) = \ln x$

In order to draw the graph of the function defined by $y = \ln x$, it is necessary to choose coordinate axes and some unit, and then for each x $(x > 0)$ to lay off the value of $\ln x$ on the perpendicular which is erected to the x-axis at the point corresponding to $(x, 0)$ on the x-axis. The ends of the perpendiculars, obtained for all possible values of x, will lie on a curve which is the graph of the *logarithmic function* (Fig. 30*a*). Below it, for comparison, Fig. 30*b* shows $\ln x$ represented as an area. In both figures the same scale is used. Taking identical values of x we can verify that the area of the curvilinear trapezoid $ACDB$ in Fig. 30*b* contains as many square units as there are linear units in the segment KL in Fig. 30*a*.

Let us note that if $0 < x' < 1$, then $\ln x'$ is a negative number, whose absolute value is equal to

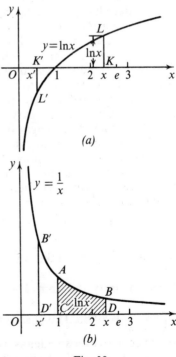

(a)

(b)

Fig. 30

39

the area of the trapezoid $B'D'CA$; because, of course, we know that

$$\ln x' = \int_1^x \frac{dx}{x} = -\int_{x'}^1 \frac{dx}{x},$$

therefore, in this case $\ln x'$ is represented in Fig. 30a by the segment $K'L'$ lying below the x-axis.

All properties of the graph of $y = \ln x$ can be deduced from the definition and properties of natural logarithms. For example, $\ln x$ is negative for $x < 1$, zero for $x = 1$, and positive for $x > 1$. Therefore, the graph of the logarithmic function lies below the x-axis for $x < 1$, intersects the x-axis at $x = 1$, and lies above the x-axis for $x > 1$. Furthermore, $y = \ln x$ increases as x increases. This is evident when $x > 1$ (see Fig. 30b), but it holds also for $x = x' < 1$. Indeed, if x' increases, but remains less than 1, then the absolute value of the area $B'D'CA$ (Fig. 30b) decreases; but this means that $\ln x$ increases, since it differs from that area only in sign.

That the logarithmic function is an increasing function is borne out by the fact that its graph is a sloping curve which rises from left to right. At first this slope is steep; then it slopes less and less. For greater clarity, we shall call the graph of the logarithmic function the *logarithmic curve*.

If we draw a horizontal path along the x-axis and follow it to the right starting from the point O, looking down at the outset we shall see an infinite abyss, in whose depths the logarithmic curve is lost. It suffices, however, to take one step of unit length in order to leave this abyss behind. Moving further along our path, we observe that with each step the curve rises higher. Thus, after two steps ($x = 2$) it reaches the height $\ln 2 \approx 0.693$, after three, $\ln 3 \approx 1.099$, etc. Let us compute how much the slope will rise when, after m steps, we take one more. Since the height of the curve after m steps (each equal to the unit length) will be $\ln m$, and after $m + 1$ steps, $\ln (m + 1)$, then after the one step the increase in the height of the curve will be:

$$\ln (m + 1) - \ln m = \ln \frac{m + 1}{m} = \ln \left(1 + \frac{1}{m}\right).$$

The more steps we take, the smaller the fraction $\frac{1}{m}$ will be, the closer to unity the sum $1 + \frac{1}{m}$ will be, and the closer to zero $\ln \left(1 + \frac{1}{m}\right)$ will be. This means that the increase in the height of the curve becomes ever smaller as we move to the right; that is, the logarithmic curve actually becomes flatter and flatter.

40

The decrease in the slope of the curve does not prevent it, however, from rising upward infinitely, so that it rises to an arbitrary height above us, if we move sufficiently far along our horizontal path. In fact, after 2^m steps the height of the curve will be equal to

$$\ln 2^m = m \cdot \ln 2 = 0.693m,$$

and this number can be made as large as we wish by taking m sufficiently large.

If, in place of the horizontal path, we draw through O a second straight-line path with some inclination α, however small (Fig. 31a), then, moving along this path, we shall sooner or later not only reach the logarithmic curve, but as we go up further, we shall leave it below us (Fig. 31b).

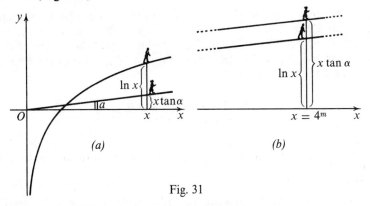

(a)   *(b)*

Fig. 31

In order to verify this, let us prove the following lemma: for any natural number m the following inequality holds:

$$\frac{4^m}{m^2} \geq 4.$$

Actually, with the increase of m by 1, the fraction $\dfrac{4^m}{m^2}$ increases, that is,

$$\frac{4^m}{m^2} < \frac{4^{m+1}}{(m+1)^2};$$

this follows from the inequality

$$\frac{\dfrac{4^{m+1}}{(m+1)^2}}{\dfrac{4^m}{m^2}} = \frac{4m^2}{(m+1)^2} = \left(\frac{2m}{m+1}\right)^2 = \left(\frac{m+m}{m+1}\right)^2 \geq 1,$$

41

true for $m \geq 1$. Therefore, among the fractions

$$\frac{4^1}{1^2}, \quad \frac{4^2}{2^2}, \quad \ldots, \quad \frac{4^m}{m^2},$$

the first is the smallest; that is, for any $m \geq 1$ it is true that

$$\frac{4^1}{1^2} \leq \frac{4^m}{m^2},$$

and this is exactly what we wanted to show.

Let us now note that for each point of the inclined, straight-line path, the relation

$$y = x \cdot \tan \alpha,$$

holds where α is the angle of inclination of the path (α is an acute angle, and consequently $\tan \alpha > 0$). If we take $x = 4^m$, then the height of the path for this x will be $4^m \cdot \tan \alpha$, and the height of the logarithmic curve will be $\ln(4^m) = m \cdot \ln 4$. The ratio of the first of these heights to the second is

$$\frac{4^m \cdot \tan \alpha}{m \cdot \ln 4} = \frac{4^m \cdot \tan \alpha}{m^2 \cdot \ln 4} m.$$

But we have shown that $\frac{4^m}{m^2} \geq 4$. Therefore the ratio of the height of the path to the height of the logarithmic curve is not less than $\frac{4 \cdot \tan \alpha}{\ln 4} m$, which, by making m sufficiently large, can be made arbitrarily large. Consequently, for $x = 4^m$ and for large m, the sloping straight-line path reaches a considerably greater height than the logarithmic curve (see Fig. 31b).

It is worth noting that the logarithmic curve has a smooth, curved shape, everywhere convex upward. We can express this property geometrically: any arc of the logarithmic curve lies above the chord of this arc (Fig. 32). Denoting by x_1 and x_2 the abscissas of the ends of an arbitrary arc $L_1 L_2$, we shall verify that for the average of the two abscissas $x = \dfrac{x_1 + x_2}{2}$, the point

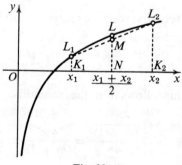

Fig. 32

L of the arc does in fact have to lie above the corresponding mid-point M of the chord.

Indeed,

$$\overline{NL} = \ln \frac{x_1 + x_2}{2}, \quad \overline{NM} = \frac{K_1 L_1 + K_2 L_2}{2}$$

(as the mid-point of the chord $L_1 L_2$), i.e.,

$$\overline{NM} = \frac{\ln x_1 + \ln x_2}{2}.$$

We must prove that

$$\ln \frac{x_1 + x_2}{2} > \frac{\ln x_1 + \ln x_2}{2}.$$

But

$$\frac{\ln x_1 + \ln x_2}{2} = \frac{1}{2} \ln (x_1 x_2) = \ln \sqrt{x_1 x_2}.$$

Therefore, it is necessary to prove that $\ln \dfrac{x_1 + x_2}{2} > \ln \sqrt{x_1 x_2}.$

We observe that

$$(\sqrt{x_1} - \sqrt{x_2})^2 = x_1 - 2\sqrt{x_1 x_2} + x_2 > 0$$

if x_1 and x_2 are two different positive numbers. Therefore,

$x_1 + x_2 > 2\sqrt{x_1 x_2}$, so that $\dfrac{x_1 + x_2}{2} > \sqrt{x_1 x_2}$ and, finally,

$$\ln \frac{x_1 + x_2}{2} > \ln \sqrt{x_1 x_2}.$$

Thus, for any arc of the graph of the logarithmic function the point of the arc corresponding to the value of the arithmetic mean of the abscissas of the ends of the arc lies above the mid-point of the chord. From this it follows that there cannot be any indentations in the logarithmic curve. For, if such an indentation existed (Fig. 33), then there would be an arc which failed to have the above property; the mid-point M of the chord would lie not below, but above the corresponding point L of the arc.

On the basis of the properties of logarithms, other interesting properties of the logarithmic curve could be deduced, but we

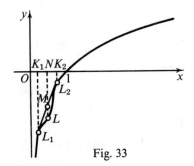

Fig. 33

shall confine our attention to those already discussed.

20. APPLICATION OF LOGARITHMS TO THE THEORY OF NUMBERS

Natural logarithms arise in the solution of many mathematical and physical problems which do not have, at first glance, any relation to areas of curvilinear trapezoids bounded by hyperbolic arcs. Here is one such problem which occupied the eminent Russian mathematician Pafnutii Lvovich Chebyshev: to find a simple formula for the approximate calculation of the number of prime numbers less than or equal to a given number n.

If n is not large, then this number is very easy to compute. We denote this number by $\pi(n)$ (the letter π used here has no relation to the well-known number 3.14159265...). Thus, if $n = 10$, the prime numbers not greater than 10 are: 2, 3, 5, 7; there are 4 of these numbers, so that $\pi(10) = 4$. If $n = 100$, then by using the method of the sieve of Eratosthenes, we can obtain 25 prime numbers: 2, 3, 5, 7, 11, 13, 17, 19, 23, 29, 31, 37, 41, 43, 47, 53, 59, 61, 67, 71, 73, 79, 83, 89, 97; consequently, $\pi(100) = 25$. If, however, n is a large number, then the problem becomes very difficult. How can one compute $\pi(n)$, even very roughly, when n is equal to a million, a billion, etc.?

Chebyshev found that to approximate the value of $\pi(n)$, it is sufficient to divide n by the natural logarithm of n:

$$\pi(n) \approx \frac{n}{\ln n};$$

the relative error of this expression (the actual error compared with the number $\pi(n)$) may be large, but approaches zero as n approaches infinity. The Chebyshev approximation is particularly convenient to apply in the case when n is a power of 10 with a positive integral exponent: $n = 10^k$. Then we obtain $\ln n = \ln 10^k = k \cdot \ln 10 \approx 2.303k$, and, consequently,

$$\pi(10^k) \approx \frac{10^k}{2.303k}.$$

Noting that $\frac{1}{2.303} \approx 0.434$, we obtain a still more convenient formula:

$$\pi(10^k) \approx 0.434 \cdot \frac{10^k}{k}.$$

Thus, for $k = 1$ and $k = 2$ we find:

$$\pi(10) \approx 0.434 \cdot 10 = 4.34 \qquad \text{(correct result 4)},$$

$$\pi(100) \approx 0.434 \cdot \frac{100}{2} \approx 21.7 \qquad \text{(correct result 25)}.$$

Continuing, we obtain:

$$\pi(1000) = 0.434 \cdot \frac{1000}{3} \approx 145 \qquad \text{(correct result 168)},$$

$$\pi(10,000) \approx 0.434 \cdot \frac{10,000}{4} \approx 1090 \qquad \text{(correct result 1229)},$$

$$\pi(10^6) \approx 0.434 \cdot \frac{10^6}{6} \approx 72,300 \qquad \text{(correct result 78,498)}.$$

The relative error of the last result amounts to

$$\frac{78,498 - 72,300}{78,498} \approx 0.08,$$

that is, 8% (of the number $\pi(10^6)$); it is still very significant. One can, however, prove with complete rigor that the relative error of the Chebyshev formula can be made arbitrarily small, if only 10^k is sufficiently large. There will come a point where it is smaller than 1%, then smaller than 0.1%, smaller than 0.001%, etc. In this fact lies the great theoretical significance of the Chebyshev formula.

P. L. Chebyshev offered still another formula for the approximate computation of $\pi(n)$, somewhat more complicated, but giving a far better approximation. The formula is the following:

$$\pi(n) \approx \int_2^n \frac{dt}{\ln t}.$$

Without carrying through the computations, we shall only indicate here some of the results:

$$\int_2^{1,000} \frac{dt}{\ln t} \approx 177 \qquad (\pi(1000) = 168),$$

$$\int_2^{10,000} \frac{dt}{\ln t} \approx 1245 \qquad (\pi(10,000) = 1229),$$

$$\int_2^{1,000,000} \frac{dt}{\ln t} \approx 78,627 \qquad (\pi(1,000,000) = 78,498).$$

The relative error of the approximation $\pi(1,000,000) \approx \int_2^{1,000,000} \frac{dt}{\ln t}$ is:

$$\frac{|78,498 - 78,627|}{78,498} \approx 0.0016, \text{ i.e., } 0.16\%.$$

21. THE NUMBER e

We saw that

$$\ln 2 \approx 0.69315 < 1, \qquad \ln 3 \approx 1.09861 > 1.$$

This means that the area of $ACDB$ (Fig. 34) is smaller than 1, while the area of ACD_1B_1 is greater than 1. One should expect that some-where between the points D and D_1, there would exist a point D' such that the area of $ACD'B'$ would be equal to 1. Such a point D' does in fact exist. If we denote $\overline{OD'}$ by the letter e, then we can assert that $2 < e < 3$. Using the table of logarithms on page 38, we can determine that $2.7 < e < 2.8$. Actually,

$$\ln 2.7 = \ln 27 - \ln 10 \approx 0.993,$$

while

$$\ln 2.8 = \ln 28 - \ln 10 \approx 1.029.$$

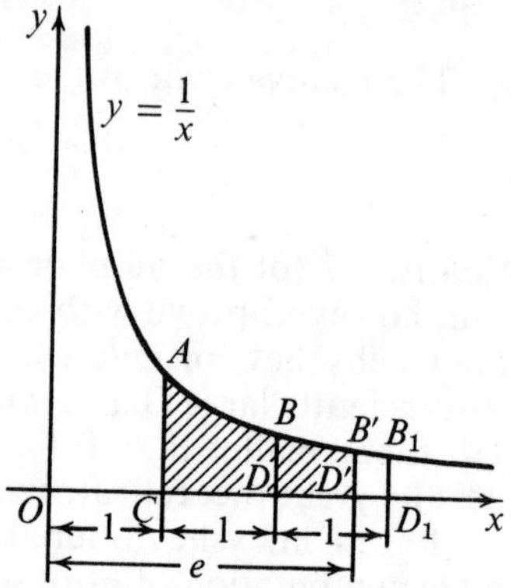

$y = \dfrac{1}{x}$

Fig. 34

There are several methods which permit one to find e with any de-sired accuracy. Without dwelling on them, we shall only indicate the result:

$$e \approx 2.7182818.$$

(All the decimal places given here are correct.) By virtue of the definition,

$$\ln e = 1.$$

The number e is called the *base* of the natural logarithms or Napier's number, after the Scottish mathematician Napier, who published the first table of logarithms (in the year 1614).

Making use of the properties of natural logarithms, we can prove the following remarkable proposition: the natural logarithm of any positive number b is the exponent of that power of the num-ber e which equals b. In other words, if $\ln b = \alpha$, then $b = e^{\alpha}$. For example, from the fact that $\ln 2 \approx 0.69315$, it follows that $2 \approx e^{0.69315}$; and since $\ln 10 \approx 2.30259$, it follows that $10 \approx e^{2.30259}$; etc.

To prove this fact, it is sufficient to make use of the property of the logarithm of powers. Let $b = e^x$; then $\ln b = \ln e^x = x \cdot \ln e$. But $\ln e = 1$; therefore $\ln b = x$; that is, the natural logarithm of b is the exponent x.

Thus, we can define natural logarithms without using geometric concepts. We could have said from the beginning that the natural logarithm of the number b is the exponent of that power of the base $e \approx 2.71828$ which equals the number b. But with such a definition it is hard to understand why we are interested in powers of the number e in particular, rather than of some other number. If we introduce natural logarithms as areas, however, their definition becomes clear, and does not give rise to any confusion.

We must add that along with natural logarithms one can introduce other logarithms having different bases. Thus, for example, the logarithm to the base 10 of the number b is the exponent of the power to which 10 must be raised to obtain b. We denote the logarithm of b to the base 10 by $\log b$. Logarithms to the base 10 are called *decimal logarithms*. If we take $\log b = \beta$, then by definition, $b = 10^{\beta}$; obviously $\log 10 = 1$. Decimal logarithms are studied at length in the second year algebra course, and all their properties are deduced not geometrically, but on the basis of known properties of exponents.

There exists a simple relation between decimal logarithms and natural logarithms. Let $\ln b = \alpha$ and $\log b = \beta$. This means that $b = e^{\alpha}$ and $b = 10^{\beta}$, i.e., $e^{\alpha} = 10^{\beta}$. Consequently, $\ln e^{\alpha} = \ln 10^{\beta}$, or $\alpha \cdot \ln e = \beta \cdot \ln 10$, i.e., $\alpha \approx \beta \cdot 2.30259$. Thus,

$$\ln b \approx 2.30259 \cdot \log b,$$

or

$$\log b \approx \frac{1}{2.30259} \cdot \ln b \approx 0.43429 \cdot \ln b.$$

Multiplying each logarithm in the table of natural logarithms by 0.43429, we obtain a table of decimal logarithms.

Thus, for example,

$$\log 2 \approx 0.43429 \cdot \ln 2 \approx 0.43429 \cdot 0.69315 \approx 0.30103.$$

For $\log 10$, we ought to obtain 1:

$$\log 10 \approx 0.43429 \cdot \ln 10 \approx 0.43429 \cdot 2.30259 \approx 1.$$

The fact that 10—the base of the decimal system of numeration —is taken as the base of decimal logarithms considerably simplifies computation with logarithms. For example, knowing that $\log 2 \approx 0.30103$ and $\log 10 = 1$, we obtain immediately:

$$\log 20 = \log 2 + \log 10 = \log 2 + 1 \approx 1.30103,$$
$$\log 200 = \log 2 + \log 100 = \log 2 + 2 \approx 2.30103, \text{ etc.}$$

On the other hand, if, knowing ln 2 ≈ 0.69315 and ln 10 ≈ 2.302585, we wish to compute ln 20 and ln 200, we must perform the following operations:

$$\ln 20 = \ln 2 + \ln 10 \approx 0.69315 + 2.30259 = 2.99574,$$
$$\ln 200 = \ln 2 + \ln 100 = \ln 2 + 2 \cdot \ln 10$$
$$\approx 0.69315 + 4.60517 = 5.29832.$$

Therefore, in using logarithms as tools for computation, the table of decimal logarithms is preferable. This does not lessen in any way the significance of natural logarithms in the solution of the most varied problems in mathematics and science. In this booklet we have discussed two mathematical problems which lead to natural logarithms—the problem of the area under an arc of an equilateral hyperbola and the Chebyshev problem of the distribution of prime numbers.

2 3 4 5 6 7 8 9